The Escape of the Giant Hogstalk

The Escape of the Giant Hogstalk

FELICE HOLMAN

Macmillan/McGraw-Hill School Publishing Company
New York Chicago Columbus

First Aladdin Books edition 1990

Aladdin Books
Macmillan Publishing Company
866 Third Avenue, New York, NY 10022
Collier Macmillan Canada, Inc.

For information regarding permission, write to
Aladdin Books, **Macmillan Publishing Company**
866 Third Avenue
New York, NY 10022
This edition is reprinted by arrangement with
Macmillan Publishing Company.

Macmillan/McGraw-Hill School Division
10 Union Square East
New York, New York 10003

Printed in the United States of America
ISBN 0-02-274959-4

1 2 3 4 5 6 7 8 9 RRC 99 98 97 96 95 94 93 92

For

LEE ANNA DEADRICK

because, among other things,
she plants small trees
where there are few
and one day there may be
a new woodland.

i

The Giant Hogstalk escaped from the Royal Botanic Gardens at Kew, England, and roamed the countryside, growing to immense size, looming up in unexpected places, frightening children and other people, too.

How could this have happened? Could it ever be captured or overcome?

One day some time ago—and no one is going to quarrel about the exact date, so why mention it—a young chemist (of sorts) named Anthony Wilson-Brown reached a surprising high point in his rather bumbling career. Even so, he did not reach it entirely by himself. He had the help and companionship of his eleven-year-old cousin, Lawrence Rockford, young Earl of Poolchester.

Even though Anthony Wilson-Brown was nearly twice the age of young Lawrence, they had a lot in common. Besides being cousins, the truth is they were both a kind of embarrassment to their families. For example, the entire Rockford family were great riders and hunters. Actually, most of their time was spent in planning the hunt, hunting, and then talking about the hunt. But young Lawrence, while he liked to ride well enough, detested the idea of killing things, and he did not even like to chase small rabbits and foxes and scare them out of their wits. So the family considered him an odd one, but of course they were fond of him anyway. Still, a Rockford who didn't hunt was very hard to explain.

The Escape of the Giant Hogstalk

And that is one reason why, when he was home on school holidays, Lawrence would go over and seek the company of his older cousin, Anthony Wilson-Brown, who did a lot of puttering around with chemicals in the basement of his house. This provided some interest and a lot of amusement for Lawrence.

Anthony Wilson-Brown (and for now we will just call him Anthony W-B, if all are agreeable) was a real embarrassment to his family, too, as anyone could see. After staining or burning nearly every piece of clothing he owned with nasty chemicals, nearly failing his final chemistry examinations, and entirely exploding the laboratory of his university (through an unfortunate error), this nice, ambitious, clumsy, chemical bungler was sent by his Wealthy Aristocratic Family for a holiday in the Caucasus, which is an out-of-the-way place (depending on where you happen to be, of course). His parents thought it would be a nice change for him, and more than that, they hoped it would give the house a chance to air out after his last very odorous experi-

ment in the basement. As an added treat, young Lawrence was sent along as a companion because, except for Lawrence, Anthony W-B was mostly a loner and had few real friends. But that is easy to explain because he was a very decent, charming-enough chap when he was not messing around with chemicals. The trouble was that he *was* mostly messing around with chemicals and then he would get all caught up in an idea and ruffle his brows and become deaf to people trying to converse with him. Then, when the things finally blew up or burned down, Anthony W-B would naturally become morose and very hard to be friendly with.

As a matter of fact, he was at his best and most likeable when he was around wild things. He liked wandering along brooks and climbing hills, and he loved flowers, cats, dogs, mice, foxes, loons, deer, snakes, and several people. So when they arrived in the Caucasus, Anthony W-B spent a lot of time roaming the wild countryside and climbing the rugged mountains. He was quite happy.

The Escape of the Giant Hogstalk

Lawrence was delighted with the vacation, too. He liked the jagged countryside, and he liked the rough people who spoke a language he couldn't understand, and what's more, nobody seemed to expect him to. They liked him and Anthony W-B, too. And Lawrence talked to Anthony W-B about it. "Do you suppose, Tony," he asked, "that it's easier to be friendly with people if you can't understand what they're saying?"

"Maybe," said Anthony W-B. "I suppose it depends on what it is they are saying that you can't understand. Don't you think?"

Lawrence thought about it. Anyhow, whatever the answer to that was, he especially liked being out of the way of the everlasting hunt that was going on at the Rockford place miles away in England— the sound of the hunting horns, the pounding of horses' hoofs, the barking of dogs, and (at least in his imagination) the frightened foxes.

"But I guess what I like best," said Lawrence one evening to Anthony W-B as they had their supper in their lodgings in a town called Novo-tsvet-lov-badzh, ". . . what I like best is not having anyone tell me what to do. How come you never tell me what to do, Tony?"

"Oh, I guess I just can't think of anything," said Anthony W-B. And then, feeling his responsibility, he added, "Or of course I would." And he settled back to eat a second honey cake, which his mother would have told him was bad for his teeth. Because, even at his age, Anthony W-B's mother worried a lot about if he ate enough of the right things or too much of the wrong ones.

Some days Lawrence and Anthony W-B did things together, and sometimes they did things separately. On this particular day Lawrence was taking a swim in his favorite cold mountain stream while Anthony W-B ambled downstream just a bit. And *that* is when he ambled right into something that was to start a chain of events that he could never have imagined.

All he was doing was ambling—just ambling, noth-

ing more—when quite suddenly an absolutely enormous "thing" seemed to leap out at him from the bushes. His first thought was that it was an animal and that he was unarmed and without so much as a cookie to charm it. But when he had cowered back from it and could view it more calmly at a slight distance, he saw that it was a plant—but such a plant! Fifteen feet or so in height! Six inches, anyway, across the stalk, upon which grew great finger-like leaves which *clutched*. And topping all this were the most enormous flower heads he had ever seen.

When he got over his initial fright he was really excited—more excited than on the day he was given his first chemistry set. "Merciful heavens!" he exclaimed. "This is certainly the biggest and most extraordinary plant that I have ever seen, without question!" And it probably was, since Anthony W-B had not been everywhere, and if there existed something larger or more extraordinary than this leaping monster of a plant, Anthony W-B had not seen it, and so he said it straight out because he was like that.

The Escape of the Giant Hogstalk

Then Anthony W-B turned around and went tearing upstream to find Lawrence and show him his discovery. But Lawrence, nearly turned to ice, had climbed out of the stream sometime before and, wrapped in towels and sweaters, had shivered his way back to the lodgings. There Anthony W-B found him defrosting in a hot tub.

"Lawrence!" Anthony W-B cried. "I've found a monstrous big plant that I want you to see."

"Tony," Lawrence said drowsily from his tub, "when I can do anything I want, forever, I'm going to build a cottage at the edge of that stream and live in it." Then he went to bed, forgetting supper, and slept until morning.

The next morning Anthony W-B roused Lawrence, who was starting to get a slight sniffle, rushed him through a good breakfast of hot goat's milk with chunks of bread floating in it, and then asked him to come look at his discovery. They packed a lunch in a knapsack, as they often did if they expected to be out for the day, and Anthony W-B sent Lawrence

The Escape of the Giant Hogstalk

hunting around the town for a small folding step-ladder. Lawrence found one without too much difficulty, which was extraordinary because he didn't know how to ask for one and the people he asked didn't know what he was asking for. But again, Lawrence found he got along very well with people when he just smiled and used a sort of private sign language. It made people laugh a lot and then they tried to help.

In this case, an old, old man found him an even older small folding ladder, but it was quite heavy. So they had to move slowly—Anthony W-B and Lawrence—weighted down as they were with the knapsack and the stepladder. It was late afternoon when they arrived at the marshy bank downstream where Anthony W-B had first seen the exotic plant. It was there all right. They approached it cautiously, but it stood there quietly now, neither leaping nor clutching.

"What do you think?" Anthony W-B asked Lawrence.

The Escape of the Giant Hogstalk

"Big," said Lawrence, and he set about opening up the folding stepladder. Then, while Lawrence steadied it, Anthony W-B climbed to its top step and, reaching up as high as he could, hacked off a flower head with Lawrence's penknife. Then he dropped the flower head into the knapsack with the leftover end of bread and sausage.

They hurried back home as fast as possible, but even so, it was dark when they arrived, quite weary, for supper. Before he went to bed that night, Anthony W-B hung the flower head on a hanger in his closet to dry. Later, before the return to England, he shook out the seeds and put them in an envelope.

However, their actual return to England had to be put off. Shortly after the flower-head hunt, Anthony W-B broke out in an odd rash of blisters on his hands and arms that itched and burned and put him out of commission for a time. But he was used to disasters and mishaps and, while he had no idea what the matter was, being a chemist (of sorts), he got a few odds and ends together and mixed them into a cooling paste to smear on the blisters. It didn't seem to make them any worse.

Lawrence was awfully sorry for Anthony W-B, of course, but he was glad of the extra vacation days and splashed about in the stream and talked a lot with the people. He was quite confused by the fact that he seemed to be able to understand them more and more, but they seemed to like him all the same.

In time, Anthony W-B's hands (which had been too blistered even to carry his luggage) were healed enough, and he and Lawrence bid farewell to the people of Novo-tsvet-lov-badzh and returned to their native land and ancestral home.

Anthony W-B was quite ready to get to work in the brand-new chemistry laboratory which, in his absence, his thoughtful parents had fixed up for him in the old carriage house some distance from the main house. Lawrence arrived home in time to miss the biggest hunt of the season and went back to school the next day. You could call the vacation a success if you want to.

The Escape of the Giant Hogstalk

But before Anthony W-B really got to work in his new chemistry laboratory, he made a call on a former classmate named Bert, who was working as a sub-sub-assistant to a biologist at the Royal Botanic Gardens at Kew.

"Look here," he said to Bert, and handed him the envelope of seeds he had brought from the Caucasus, "these are seeds from the largest plant I have ever seen. Not being a botanist, but a chemist, I haven't a notion what the plant is. But, see here, you're a biologist. . . ."

"I'm a sub-sub-biologist. . . ." complained Bert.

"Never mind," said Anthony W-B. "What I think you should do is grow these in one of your greenhouses and you may be able to identify the plant. Might make you a *sub*-biologist," he added as a sneaky sort of incentive.

"How tall did you say?" asked Bert.

"At least fifteen feet."

"G'wan!" said Bert, who liked but had no special reason to rely on his old classmate, Anthony W-B,

The Escape of the Giant Hogstalk

whose reputation for getting things wrong was widespread.

"Truly," said Anthony W-B, "and six inches across the stalk. As for the flower heads . . . well, you wouldn't believe them!"

"I'll tell you, Tony," said Bert. "I don't really believe the whole thing. I think you were sleepwalking. Those mountain heights can do queer things to you. Or else you're kidding me. . . ."

"Would I fool you, Bert?" asked Anthony W-B plaintively. And Bert had to admit to himself that old Tony was not best known for his sense of humor.

More to oblige his former classmate than for any other reason, Bert, still doubting the tale, took just one of the seeds from the envelope and planted it in a little flowerpot. He put it in a corner of the greenhouse that was in his charge and watered it. The rest of the seeds he put in a drawer and labeled the envelope **? ?**. It seemed that he had hardly turned his back when the seed began to grow. As a matter of fact, it didn't seem to grow, it seemed to explode.

The Escape of the Giant Hogstalk

One minute there was nothing but earth in the little pot, and the next minute there was the beginning of a plant. That's what Bert said, anyhow. Within a very short time, Bert found it necessary to move the plant to a larger pot. And then to a larger one. And a larger one. And when he had moved it to the largest pot available in Kew, he decided to consult a sub-biologist. The sub-biologist examined the plant carefully, and when he heard it had grown to such a size in so short a time, he said, "It's big," and went to consult the Chief Biologist.

The Chief Biologist knew his stuff. He took one look at the plant, now outgrowing its pot, and said, "Bless my soul!" which is the sort of thing Chief Biologists can get away with, even today. "Bless my soul!" he said. "Unless my eyes deceive me, that is a specimen of the exotic Giant Hogstalk. We have never had a plant of that kind in the Royal Botanic Gardens. Wherever did it come from?"

"An old school chum of mine, named Anthony Wilson-Brown, found the thing growing wild in the

The Escape of the Giant Hogstalk

Caucasus . . . or so he says," said Bert stepping forward. "He brought me some seeds and I planted just the one."

"Bring him here!" commanded the Chief Biologist, and then he went himself to ring up Buckingham Palace and ask the Queen to please and kindly have a suitable medal engraved for Anthony Wilson-Brown.

The Queen called the Royal Medal Engraver and he rummaged around until he found something appropriate—a gold medal etched with a general sort of flower with a handsome shield in the background. He polished it up and engraved the right thing on the reverse side, hung it on a blue and white striped ribbon, and pinned it into a velvet-lined case.

"Anthony Wilson-Brown, in the name of Her Majesty, I bestow upon you this medal, making you a member of the exclusive Society of Royal Biologists—Weed-Seed Division."

"But I am a chemist!" protested Anthony W-B,

half rising from his red velvet chair. The Chief
Biologist pushed him down again. Lawrence waved
at him proudly from the small audience.

"By the power invested in me by Her Majesty, I
now pronounce you A Distinguished Man."

*And that was the height, the pinnacle, the peak,
the apex, the zenith, of the career of Anthony Wilson-
Brown, until then.*

ii

Meanwhile, the Giant Hogstalk kept growing and began to sway slightly in the luscious green heat of the Royal Botanic Gardens hothouse.

At first Anthony W-B, still stunned by the first success of his life, came to look at the Giant Hogstalk and refresh himself in the wonderful feeling of accomplishment. He came every other day, not wishing to make himself conspicuous. He would never go directly to the greenhouse where the Giant Hogstalk grew. He was devious. Sometimes he would enter the Royal Botanic Gardens by the Cumberland Gate and amble around the scree beds, then idle a while under the Japanese Cherries, make his way up the path to the Turkey Oak, and then scoot over the lawns for a good look at his Giant Hogstalk. He would stare at it through the cloudy windows of the greenhouse and wonder at its prodigious growth. He wished Lawrence could get back from school to see it.

Another day he would enter by the Victoria Gate and go straight up the path as if going to visit the Palm House. He would linger in front of this enormous and elegant structure, staring at each of the Queen's Beasts, carved in stone, which guard the Palm House. Then he would wander over to the pond and watch the fountain splashing over a statue of Hercules and spend a few minutes observing the carp and eels that slipped about in the oily green water. Then he would make a completely extraneous side-trip to the Orangery, take a look at the Filmy Fern House, and then once again scoot across the lawns to the Giant Hogstalk. And so forth. It helped to build his ego and made him feel a little better on days that things went especially wrong in his new carriage-house laboratory.

But then something started to bother him about the Giant Hogstalk. He couldn't say just what it was. At first he tried to ignore it. He took a different route—stopped at the refreshment pavilion for tea, took the long way around by the Boathouse Walk, and approached the Giant Hogstalk from another direction. No, there was no question about it. The good feeling was fading. Anthony W-B had never been very good at expressing himself, which in this case was just as well, but he finally came to feel that the plant *bore him a grudge*. He cut his visits

The Escape of the Giant Hogstalk

down to once a week . . . then, every other week
. . . and finally not at all.

His friend Bert took a kind of dislike to the
plant, too. It had something to do with the unquench-
able thirst of the thing, with its wild rate of growth,
and now, its subtle swaying, and . . . well, he didn't
mention a few other things that bothered him about it.

But very soon it became evident that something
new and threatening had developed as the plant grew
to maturity. It seemed that if one touched the plant,
most particularly after it had had a drink of water,
it caused one to break out in nasty blisters—sometimes
painful—or dreadful rashes that itched more than they
hurt, and hurt more than they itched. Bert and two
other sub-sub-biologists were afflicted as well as three
general keepers.

At that point, the Chief Biologist decided to give
the plant its very own keeper. The keeper, an elderly
man named Oliver Buskin, had always had a way
with plants. He studied the problem carefully and
then managed it quite handily. He dressed himself

The Escape of the Giant Hogstalk

in a sort of rubber diving suit and simply took charge. No nonsense! He tended the Giant Hogstalk as if it were a wild animal in a zoo—dancing around it spryly in his rubber suit, watering the plant with a long hose, and tending and pruning it with tools attached to long poles which he himself had invented for the purpose. With these he sparred and fenced with the Giant Hogstalk, and for a while at least it looked as if he had it under control.

But even so, the keeper, old O. Buskin, felt both dislike and pride regarding his charge. He was proud because it *was* his charge and one of the largest plants in all of Kew, in all of the British Isles, perhaps, and possibly in the world, for all he knew. It was, so to speak, his child, though a difficult one. On the other hand, even if it was a special plant, and big, and not bad-looking, it did keep swaying in an increasingly threatening way, and growing secretly . . . almost sneakily. It was getting inordinately spready and inordinately tall. There was no question about that. The Chief Biologist, on one of his inspections, said,

The Escape of the Giant Hogstalk

"Fence it in. It's getting out of hand." And so the Royal Botanic Gardens' carpenters and metal workers built a sort of corral around it. Buskin, though he still had the upper hand, felt that the corral only made the Giant Hogstalk more sullen and malevolent.

Back in his private chemistry laboratory, Anthony W-B had started once again to putter around with vials and potions. There was a minor disaster that had to do with an idea for making pure alcohol out of hard-boiled eggs. He never got beyond the hard-boiled egg stage of the experiment. Cooking was something he had not been taught, and he allowed the water to cook away in the pot. While the pot simply burned, the eggs (with the luck of Anthony W-B) exploded. They hung in thousands of yellow and white clusters all over the laboratory. It was a real wonder that anything as small as a few eggs could make such a mess, and the smell was something to reckon with. Anthony W-B made some efforts to clear it up but it seemed that there would

The Escape of the Giant Hogstalk

always be some egg left in the carriage house. As it happened, there wasn't.

The reason there wasn't is this. Anthony W-B failed again in his efforts to make writing paper out of carrot scrapings, but this was only a mess and not really any kind of crisis. He put his medal of the Order of the Royal Biologists—Weed-Seed Division in a prominent place on the wall of the laboratory to help his morale, but it did little to cheer him when he failed in his fourth attempt to make strikeless kitchen matches. They were meant to light by simply taking them from the box and waving them in the air. However, for reasons unknown, they ignited *in* their box. This resulted in a small fire which became a large fire and burned down the whole carriage house, and with it the remains of the exploded eggs.

Now this was the kind of time when Anthony W-B would become his *most* unsociable, and he just wandered around the countryside alone. This time his patient parents began to set up another new

The Escape of the Giant Hogstalk

laboratory for him at the very edge of the grounds in the old gamekeeper's cottage. And, since it was now the long school holiday, joining Anthony W-B on these post–strikeless-match-disaster wanderings was young Lawrence. Together they walked through the high meadows and the low meadows while the new laboratory was being made ready: They didn't talk much because Lawrence had learned that it was best not to bother Anthony W-B too much when he was in a blue funk, and this was a fairly blue one. But Lawrence did a lot of thinking and one of the things he thought was that chemistry looked like fun sometimes and often seemed a good idea, too, but it didn't seem to work out very well, did it. And he wondered, too, what he himself might do in the world if he wasn't going to hunt.

If, in their walks, the horn of the hunt sounded and the horses were seen galloping over the fields in pursuit of the hapless fox, Lawrence and Anthony W-B would turn their backs sadly on the scene. A few times Lawrence had been able to get up early and cleverly lay a false scent for the hounds. It worked and made a mess of the hunt for the day. The trouble was that he had to use the tail of the fox that had been brought home the day before. Lawrence just hated to do that. Then, during one particular walk, he got a keen idea.

"Tony," he said, breaking the silence, "do you suppose you could invent a *fake* false fox scent to fool the dogs?"

Anthony W-B muttered that he didn't see why not and that he would certainly make a try at it as soon as he finished his next project.

It didn't take Anthony W-B very long to recover from his latest failure. He was used to failure and used to getting over failure, and so he pitched in again. Although he knew it had been tried by others without success, Anthony W-B now set about concocting The Elixir of Life—a potion to keep people going on and on, no matter how rotten they felt. Anthony W-B had a cheerful hunch he could do it.

iii

Meanwhile, back at the Royal Botanic Gardens, the keeper thought the Giant Hogstalk had begun to make a sound—a sort of groaning, or moaning, or possibly growling, it was hard to be sure. Just when he thought he had heard it, it would stop and not begin again until the keeper was nearly out of hearing.

Then one night, when not a soul was about, except the night attendant (and he asleep in the Palm House), the Giant Hogstalk did something no one had thought of. It grew another inch, pushed its head against the glass top of the greenhouse . . . and heaved!

The tinkling of glass was not heard by the attendant in the Palm House. Now the Giant Hogstalk, which must have been hunching its shoulders until then, stood up entirely straight and, quite without anyone knowing or dreaming of it, allowed a great many seeds—which may henceforth be called "shoats"—to escape over the top and down the sides of the greenhouse. The shoats slid down easily on the glass surface and a light breeze started them on their unsuspected, undetected, sneaky escape, which was to take some of them quite a distance.

The next morning there was a lot of confusion, some suspicions, a few accusations, but in the end the carpenters and blacksmiths and glaziers just went about repairing the greenhouse, reinforcing it with metal bars and double glass. The Chief Biologist himself supervised the installation of a tricky lock and forbade anyone except Authorized Personnel to enter. It took two keys to open the lock and no person had both keys. It was a very tight security thing.

The Escape of the Giant Hogstalk

After that, under cover of darkness or in the misty English mornings, the many shoats blew quietly and secretly from place to place over the countryside, finding their way to marshy ground along streams and brooks. Then during an early fall rainstorm, they dug in wherever they happened to be.

All winter Anthony W-B worked on his Elixir of Life, whistling at first, as he added tincture of this and tincture of that to sodium something-or-other and potassium such-and-such. Now and then he would glance up at his somewhat charred gold medal to cheer him on. The velvet case and the blue and white ribbon had been completely burned up in the carriage house fire, but Anthony W-B had put a string through the gold link and had polished off most of the char. A medal was still a medal, after all. But eventually he stopped whistling as one elixir after the other failed to be The Elixir of Life. Indeed, they seemed to be nothing more or less than, at best, chocolate malts and, at worst, bad medicine. The mice on whom he tried the elixirs lapped up most of

them, since Anthony W-B liked his potions to taste good. Usually the mice showed no noticeable effects at all, but sometimes they did seem to get just a bit dizzy or sometimes sleepy. Once a mouse ran in circles for an hour. At first this looked like the most hopeful sign of all, but it turned out to be a passing symptom. And Anthony W-B had to admit, that even if it had turned out to be The Elixir of Life, a side effect causing one to run in circles for an entire endless life would not be a totally successful elixir.

As for young Lawrence, he was back at his school playing football and learning Latin and algebra. It was all right, but not as peaceful and diverting as sitting around watching Anthony W-B make his potions and small disasters in the laboratory. But then at the Christmas holidays, when Lawrence came home from school, he trudged over to call on his cousin. He was especially eager for Anthony W-B to finish up on that old elixir and get going on the fake false fox scent. He arrived just in time to see the mouse running in circles and wait for the results.

"I guess that's not it. Right?" Lawrence ventured.

"Right," said Anthony W-B. And that was the usual extent of their conversational turns at times like these. After that failure, of course, Lawrence knew from experience that Anthony W-B was not going to be very good company for a while. But he had an idea.

"I say, Tony," he said. "Do you suppose you could let me have a bit of this and that, and I might try and get something started on that fake false fox scent, you know?"

"Well, I don't know . . ." Anthony W-B said doubtfully. "This stuff can be tricky, you know."

"I know," said Lawrence. "But scents shouldn't blow up or catch fire, do you think?"

"No, I shouldn't think so," said Anthony W-B. "Although you never can tell. Might smell things up a bit, if they don't mind over at your house."

"I'll find a place in the basement," said Lawrence, seeing he had sold his cousin on the idea.

The Escape of the Giant Hogstalk

"Right!" said Anthony W-B, and he began to collect some bottles and vials and beakers and test tubes and some basic chemicals for young Lawrence. "Basement. That's just where I got my start," he said encouragingly.

So young Lawrence spent most of the Christmas holiday down in the basement. As his cousin had instructed him, he scribbled down the formula for every new batch he mixed. And he did work up a lot of scents, but none of them was really foxy. No Rockford had a hint of what he was up to, although his mother did say on Christmas Eve when they were trimming the tree, "I think there may have been a skunk around this tree before it was cut," so Lawrence stayed out of her way. He thought, happily, that if it did smell skunkish, he might be getting close to what he wanted. But before he could get any closer it was time to go back to school. The rest of the work would have to wait until the long spring holiday in April.

iv

Surprisingly, after its violent break-out, the Giant Hogstalk seemed to quiet down. It swayed less, behaved well, and its keeper found it more docile in all ways. It seemed, he thought, to be actually smiling. But when he told this to the Orchid Keeper, the Orchid Keeper said, "You're getting dotty, Buskin," so Oliver Buskin didn't tell anyone else, because if you can't trust an Orchid Keeper, whom can you trust?

Early spring was lovely and the long spring holiday saw the children of England turned loose over the countryside for good times—games, picnics, bird watching—things like that, one supposes. But one cannot suppose everything, and no one could possibly be expected to suppose what actually happened.

Two perfectly nice children, named John and Kate Nokwould, wandering from their country cottage one afternoon, emerged from a woody spot onto a large marsh meadow and started an ordinary-enough game of hide-and-seek amid the hedgerows.

Kate saw it first and screamed. Her scream gave her hiding place away and John called, "I spy!" before he realized that Kate was standing with one arm clamped over her eyes and her other trembling arm pointing at something. John followed the direction of her pointing arm and saw, about two feet away, what seemed to be just a rather large stalk of a plant. Then his eyes followed the stalk upwards . . . upwards to enormous spreading leaves . . . and then way up to four giant heads which swayed and, as John said later, *grunted*.

The Escape of the Giant Hogstalk

"It jumped out at me! It jumped out at me!" Kate screamed. John grabbed her hand and they both ran home as fast as they could. But when they told all this to their mother at teatime, she laughed and said, "Such charming imaginations!" and gave them each an extra cookie.

However, that very morning, miles away, Mary and Matilda Blunt had gone out early for a picnic breakfast. It was one of the things they liked to do best—walk out when everyone was still asleep and the grass still dewy. The breakfast was good—they had packed it themselves—muffins and jam, milk, and an apple for each. After the picnic they decided to collect some wild flowers for their mother. They made a nice bouquet, and to frame it they picked the lower leaves from a medium-large plant. The leaves were unusual—like fingers—and spectacularly large. In picking them they discovered that the plant had a hollow stem.

"Ooh, what a wonderful bean shooter!" cried

The Escape of the Giant Hogstalk

Mary, and quickly, in her clever creative way, she stripped the leaves from two stems. Then, into each hollow stem she put a pine nut from a packet she kept in her pocket for midmorning snacks. She gave one of the "bean shooters" to Matilda and the children popped pine nuts at each other for a cheerful half hour, then lost interest and went home.

The next day Mary and Matilda both had great red circles of blisters around their mouths and rashes on their hands. They were a couple of miserable English children. They had to spend hours of each day under wet compresses, while their mother read stories to them (which all turned out to have sneaky messages and morals or else taught them things they didn't know—the coastal mileage of the African continent and things about icebergs and glaciers).

So now we have John and Kate Nokwould scared solid, and Mary and Matilda Blunt itching and in pain under wet compresses, being read useful things. Not really causes for a national panic. Yet at that time, it was not possible to say how many blistered

The Escape of the Giant Hogstalk

children and other people there may have been in England. The cases were scattered and only a few were reported. They did not seem to be connected in any way . . . then. But one by one they began to pile up in reports to the Ministry of Health. Most were very much like Mary, Matilda, John, and Kate. Others were more dramatic. A prisoner had made a clever escape from Borstal and had managed to stay hidden in the woods for three days. It was in all the newspapers. But then he turned himself in to the prison infirmary when the itching and burning of a mysterious rash became too much to bear. Prison seemed better at the moment.

It took young Lawrence Rockford to really tip the scales and cause a hue and cry to be raised. The family had gone to their shooting lodge for a long weekend. Lawrence, wishing he were back in the basement at home and wanting, at any rate, to get out of sight of the shooting, wandered out into the lower field. It was there that this enormous swaying thing seemed to spring out of the hedges and leap toward him.

The Escape of the Giant Hogstalk

When he got over his initial surprise and fright (which he never admitted to, since shooting families are not given to frights), he recovered his poise and regarded the plant from a distance. It was pretty tall, but not as tall as the one Cousin Tony had got the medal for. *The one Cousin Tony had got the medal for!* It *was* rather the same sort of plant, wasn't it? Hey! He reached into his pocket for his penknife and cut off a branch, thinking to take it to show Tony. But when he saw the hollow stem it gave him an idea. He cut another branch to take home to show Anthony W-B, then he stripped the leaves from the first stalk and made a long hollow sort of tube. Then he put it to his eye and used it as a telescope. He viewed the quiet meadows and lowlands through this long thin peephole. It was quite interesting for a few minutes. Then he went home, taking the telescope and the branch. No one seemed very interested in it, at first. They were still arguing about who had bagged the largest trophy.

In the morning Lawrence had what seemed to be a

black eye coming on. It certainly hurt, or itched, or both. Then, it was clearly *not* a black eye, and *then* they got interested in the telescope, *and then*. . . .

Anthony W-B added a bit of sugar to the newest elixir and then placed it on a table outside the carriage house to subject it to the beneficial rays of the sun. This was a new idea he had and he felt pretty cheerful about it, for the moment. He poured himself a glass of tonic water and sat in a chair beside the table (where he could keep an eye on the elixir) and started to read the *London Daily Enquirer*.

GIANT HOGSTALK ESCAPES FROM ROYAL BOTANIC GARDENS

. . . he read. Anthony W-B felt as if he had been suddenly cast in iron, but he went on to read the miserable details.

"Scores of cases of a mysterious skin poisoning have been traced to a new breed of plant now rampant

The Escape of the Giant Hogstalk

in the fields of England. Many people, especially
children, have been stricken, and physicians and
clinics are besieged by calls asking how to treat
this most unpleasant condition. The plant has been
identified as the Giant Hogstalk, a recent acquisition
of the Royal Botanic Gardens. Just how the
plant has managed to spread is unknown at this
time. The Chief Biologist at Kew, having identified
the specimens brought to his attention, refused further
comment. A guard at one of the greenhouses
did remark to this reporter, "They do blame everything
on Kew, don't they!" People are warned, for
the present, to stay clear of a plant of the following
description . . . (*a description of the Hogstalk followed*)
and to report its location to a central headquarters
now being organized by the Royal Biologists
in cooperation with the Ministry of Health."

Royal Biologists! Now Anthony W-B *was* despondent.
His one success was clearly just another
disaster. And would he also lose his membership in

The Escape of the Giant Hogstalk

the Society of Royal Biologists—Weed-Seed Division?
Thinking morosely of this possibility and then of all
the ailing children and other people of England,
Anthony W-B did not notice that he had drunk up
his elixir instead of his tonic water. Later he fed
the tonic to the mice and they liked it a lot.

V

In the greenhouse at the Royal Botanic Gardens, the captive Giant Hogstalk had become nearly complacent. It caused no trouble at all, but its keeper felt, nevertheless, that it "sneered," though he did not tell that to anyone (least of all the Orchid Keeper). However, he knew he was right about it, just as he had been right about it smiling earlier on.

But in the houses of Parliament and all over England a real crisis was developing. The Royal Physicians were talking to the Prime Minister, and the Prime Minister was talking to the Queen, and the Queen was talking to her Chancellors, and the Queen's Chancellors were talking to the Royal Biologists, and the Royal Biologists were wringing their hands, most particularly the Chief Biologist at Kew, as more and more Giant Hogstalk sightings and cases were reported. It seemed that it was not necessary to make telescopes or bean shooters to come down with a good case of Hogstalk poisoning. All one needed to do was take an innocent walk and, quite without knowing it, brush up against any part of the dangerous plant, even if it was young and not fully grown or in flower. The most especially perilous times were in the early morning while the dew was still on the leaves, or on a misty day, or after a rain. They grew tallest and fastest in marshy ground.

So someone just shortcutting across a low field on the way to work, or squeezing past a hedgerow to let a car go by, or spending a quiet morning fishing, ran the ever-increasing danger of knowing the poisonous touch of the Giant Hogstalk. There continued to be reports of some "leaping" or "grunting," and the Royal Biologists, who were now organized to handle the situation, related that to the size of the plant. Larger plants seemed more likely to grunt and leap than less developed plants. They thought that perhaps the weather or the position of the sun might have something to do with it, too, but the whole thing was vague and entirely unscientific. What had to be dealt with immediately was *getting rid of the Giant Hogstalk.*

The Evening News carried an editorial stating, "Here is a challenge to the New Government. What does the Prime Minister intend to do about the Giant Hogstalk? The growth of the Hogstalk must take precedence over the growth in the cost of living."

In response to this and other demands, the Royal Biologists declared a Giant Hogstalk hunt. The hunt was divided into counties and boroughs and towns

The Escape of the Giant Hogstalk

and villages. Maps were provided for all areas and citizen volunteers were organized into teams. They ranged in age from children of eight to men of eighty. Most everyone wore rain gear or odds and ends of hunting clothes. They were peculiar-looking groups as they gathered for instructions. Most groups hunted like this: they would stretch out across an area of a field, join hands, and then comb each foot of ground as if hunting an escaped criminal. Whenever a Giant Hogstalk was found, the leader of the team, wearing protective clothing, would throw a bag over the flower heads (to prevent their dropping seeds) and then hack the plant off at its base. Then the team would rejoin and continue the hunt.

But though many Giant Hogstalks of various sizes were found and felled, the escaped shoats of the Hogstalk at Kew were numerous and devious. No matter how many were cut down, there seemed always to be more. And though men, women, and children raked the marshes, fields, and hedgerows for weeks, and though cheers went up every time a Giant Hog-

The Escape of the Giant Hogstalk

stalk was routed out and chopped to the ground, it finally had to be admitted that the end was not in sight.

"A Hogstalk here and a Hogstalk there is not going to solve a nationwide problem," the Prime Minister told the Queen. The Queen said he was right, and he was.

But there were other volunteers. A very rich man in Texas, U.S.A., misunderstood the situation and sent his very own private plane across the Atlantic Ocean carrying America's champion hog-caller from Arkansas. The hog-caller, his hands cupped to his mouth, spent several days tramping about Buckinghamshire calling, "Ooeee, ooeee!" in the best tradition of Arkansas hog-callers. When he turned over to the Society of Royal Biologists twelve small porkers from neighborhood farms, he was not met with the gratitude he thought he deserved. However, they did escort him back to the private plane and send a thank-you note to the man in Texas.

One of the Royal Biologists had an idea he thought was really fine. He sent for the Public Health Di-

The Escape of the Giant Hogstalk

rector of the Caucasus, which was where the plant originally had come from, after all. This man was not easy to find. The Caucasus turned out to be not only very far away but very complicated geographically and politically. The Public Health Director lived in a hut on a very tall mountain that could only be reached by a mule trail. But he came. It was a long trip and when it was done it did seem that the Royal Biologist might just have written a letter or sent a cable. That, at least, is what the Chancellor of the Exchequer said. Because the Caucasian Health Director listened to the story and then he said gravely (in Caucasian, which meant the added cost of an interpreter), "In the Caucasus, when we see a Giant Hogstalk, we stay away from it." And then he left.

vi

There was no question now, in O. Buskin's mind, about the sneering of his Giant Hogstalk. And of course, now he knew why. In spite of its imprisonment (so to speak) and despite the elaborate care, the Giant Hogstalk had managed to send out its offspring—the shoats—to populate the British Isles. Yes, Buskin felt oddly proud of his ornery Hogstalk, but then, just sometimes, just a bit sorry for it. "Watch it!" he would say to himself at those times. "You'll lose the upper hand, Buskin." But he also began to wonder now if he really ever had the upper hand.

Spring holidays were coming to an end and young Lawrence, having given up hope of Anthony W-B getting around to the fake false fox scent, was working like mad himself. He had borrowed a few of his mother's perfumes and colognes, added them to the fairly successful skunk scent, watered it down a bit, and thought he might be well on his way to the fox scent. The perfume called *Love Me Truly* was too heavy. He left that out of the next mix. Something called *Luxurie #10*, which came in a very small bottle, was very good, really sharp and foxy. He tried *Deep Night*, which was no good at all, and *Forest Dream*, which had a good name and should have been right but wasn't. In the end, *Luxurie #10* proved best. He added some oil for a base and then a good shake of turpentine. He felt just about ready to consult Anthony W-B.

Despite the advice of the Caucasian Public Health Director to stay away from the plant and despite the great Hogstalk hunts, cases of itching and blisters

The Escape of the Giant Hogstalk

continued to be reported. The arguments in Parliament continued, the articles in the newspapers persisted, the wireless and the television blared on. Anthony W-B tried without luck to close his ears to it all and went back to improving his basic Elixir of Life. He felt rotten. He listlessly mixed magnesium whatchamacallit with chloride of somethingorother, faithfully writing it all down in his messy, stained pocket diary, which contained the ingredients of all his experiments, including the one which had burned down the carriage house. His diary was always in his pocket, just in case he got an idea while walking.

These days he did quite a lot of walking—as much walking as working, in fact, because he was that depressed. One day, after a walk out over the high meadows, Anthony W-B made his return to the gamekeeper's cottage through a little woods, across a small brook, and then just a step to the back of the cottage laboratory. And there—right there—not two feet from the laboratory, Anthony W-B saw his second Giant Hogstalk. How had he missed it before,

The Escape of the Giant Hogstalk

he asked himself. It was right in a line with the window. The answer was simple and he knew it. When at work in the laboratory, Anthony W-B always wore his reading and close-work glasses. The Hogstalk was out of focus if he chanced to look out the window. That explained that. But nevertheless there it was, and he thought it had best be chopped down. However, after his case of blisters in the Caucasus (now that he knew their cause), he decided he would not do the chopping without some protective clothing. He walked carefully around it. It was not as big as the one he had seen in the Caucasus, but it *was* pretty big. Good thing no one ever walked that way, he thought, and hurried into the lab.

As he opened the door he glanced sorrowfully at his charred medal, then put on his glasses and reached for the calcium propionate. Now *this* was the new idea he had. Calcium propionate is used a great deal as a preservative in foods—breads, for example. Now if a *little* of this chemical would work to preserve foods for a while, why wouldn't a *lot* of it work to preserve people for even longer! Anyhow, that's the way Anthony W-B's mind was going at that time. He was about to add a good spoonful to his basic elixir when young Lawrence burst into the laboratory.

"Cousin Tony!" he shrieked. "I think I've got it. Here, smell!"

"Got what?" asked Anthony W-B absently.

"The fake false fox scent. I think I've got it!" And as he spoke, Lawrence pushed the test tube of scent up under Anthony W-B's nose just as Anthony W-B was moving the measure of calcium propionate to the large beaker of elixir.

"Lawrence!" he snapped in real annoyance. "Not now! You're in my way."

Startled, and not wishing to upset Anthony W-B, Lawrence pulled his test tube of scent away from Anthony W-B's face quickly—too quickly. At just that moment Anthony W-B's hand, balancing the chemical and moving in the same direction, collided with the test tube of fake false fox scent and tipped the entire tube, glass and all, into the beaker of elixir,

The Escape of the Giant Hogstalk

along with the measure of calcium propionate.

Lawrence was horrified, frightened . . . and disappointed. (*His* fox scent, after all!) But Anthony W-B was furious. He took the beaker and, bringing it back over his head, heaved the entire mess—elixir, fox scent, beaker, test tube, and measuring spoon—through the open window. It was a fit of temper that he hardly ever allowed himself. Then he turned to Lawrence.

"You . . . you . . . pipsqueak!" he yelled. "You basement chemist! That was my Elixir of Life—the one that could work. Weeks of work for nothing . . . nothing." He started sinking into one of his blue funks.

"But Tony," said Lawrence, "can't you make it again? I mean you must have kept the formula. I mean I would go home and make mine over again right now except that I've used up all the *Luxurie #10* and I haven't enough money left from my allowance to buy any more. Believe me, Tony, I feel worse than you do."

The Escape of the Giant Hogstalk

For the first time in his fairly quiet life Anthony W-B, struck by still another disappointment, full of guilt for his part in the fate of the people of England, and reeking with some spilled fake false fox scent, felt like punching someone in the nose. Young Lawrence was used to that look on people's faces. He often saw it at school. He moved out of range and in the direction of the window. He was just in time to see an extraordinary sight.

"Tony! Tony!" he called. "Come quick!"

Anthony W-B didn't budge. He was sinking deeper and deeper into the bluer and bluer funk that regularly followed chemical disasters.

"But Tony, you must! There's a Giant Hogstalk right out here!"

"I know that," Anthony W-B answered in a blue voice. "I saw it earlier today."

"But it's doing something . . . something funny!"

"They sway," muttered Anthony W-B.

"It's not swaying. It's . . . it's . . . oh, please, Tony. Come!" Then Lawrence came over and physically

The Escape of the Giant Hogstalk

dragged Anthony W-B to the window in time to see the Giant Hogstalk slowly, slowly, slowly fold itself up like an accordion and slump to the ground.

Lawrence and Anthony W-B looked at each other, then back at the crumpled Hogstalk. Then, as one, they turned and squeezed through the doorway together and raced around the side of the cottage to view the felled villain.

Lawrence was the first to recover. "I . . . I say, Tony, look at all the glass around it. Do you suppose that when you threw the beaker of . . . of stuff, you could have wounded it? Like, stabbed it?"

Anthony W-B considered the idea but quickly discarded it. "No. It would have had to cut off the roots or the main stem. This main stem is in one piece. Look, there aren't any cuts on it. Anyhow, the beaker would probably have broken on the ground. See, all the pieces are around the bottom of the plant. It must have fallen close to the Hogstalk and broken and spilled out the elixir onto the roots."

The Escape of the Giant Hogstalk

"*And* the fake false fox scent!" cried Lawrence.

"Spilled out the elixir . . ." Anthony W-B repeated slowly. Then he said it quickly . . . much more quickly and loudly, "*Spilled out the elixir!*"

"*And* the fake false fox scent," mourned Lawrence, now enough of a chemist to get the idea.

"And poisoned it!" cried Anthony W-B. "Merciful heavens! Merciful heavens, we may have found the way to get rid of the Giant Hogstalk!" He examined the plant more closely. "See, some of this mixture has splashed up onto the leaves. Ha! Aha! Quickly, Lawrence, go back to your lab and get your formula and put it together exactly as you did. I'll get started putting my last Elixir of . . . oh dear. . . ." He looked stricken. "It may *not* have been The Elixir of Life, after all."

Lawrence stopped on his way out the door. "But the *Luxurie #10* . . ." he said.

"That can't matter," said Anthony W-B with certainty. "It's only an aroma, not an active chemical." But then he saw how disappointed Lawrence looked

The Escape of the Giant Hogstalk

and he said, "Very well. If it worries you, here are a couple of pounds. Run down to the chemist and get some. And Lawrence . . ." he said. Lawrence stopped once more in his dash out the door. "Lawrence . . ." Anthony W-B started again. And then all in a rush he said, "I'm sorry I called you a basement chemist."

vii

A twenty-four-hour watch had been put on the Giant Hogstalk at the Royal Botanic Gardens. Oliver Buskin kept the day shift and he kept it well. Now people came to Kew just to see the Hogstalk, and O. Buskin felt that he and his Hogstalk were in this, somehow, together. As people peered through the windows, O. Buskin felt that, dangerous or not, his Hogstalk was a feature attraction and that he, old Oliver Buskin, was something of a celebrity. (It was not his fault, after all, if the Orchid Keeper was jealous.)

The Escape of the Giant Hogstalk

While the Queen was wringing her hands at Buckingham Palace, and the Prime Minister was wringing his at Number Ten Downing Street, and the Royal Biologists were all wringing theirs (most especially at Kew), and the hog-caller was winging his way back to Arkansas, and the Caucasian Public Health Director was heading for his mountaintop, Anthony W-B and young Lawrence were not letting any grass grow under their feet, nor any Hogstalk, either. Within hours Anthony W-B had put together a sizeable beaker of the same basic elixir that it had taken him weeks to develop originally, and added the calcium propionate. Lawrence was doing the same thing with the fake false fox scent back in his family's basement. For a few minutes he worried terribly that there was not enough turpentine, but then he found a can of something without a label which turned out to be almost positively more turpentine.

By mid-afternoon Lawrence was back at the laboratory with his beaker of fresh fake false fox scent. "Here it is!" he shouted, as he skidded into the lab. "Shall I dump it in?"

The Escape of the Giant Hogstalk

"No, no!" cried Anthony W-B. "Not yet. We have to be very scientific about this. *Very* scientific. This has to be a controlled experiment, but time is important, too. Now, I'm going to divide the elixir in this beaker into two parts." And he poured part of the elixir into another beaker and labeled the beakers, "#1" and "#1A."

"Now let's do the same thing with your scent." He reached for the beaker that Lawrence was holding. Lawrence was mystified.

"But why?" he asked. "What's all the fuss about? We just heaved them both together last time, didn't we? It worked, didn't it? We invented something!"

Anthony W-B, made cautious by his many disappointments, restrained his enthusiasm. "We'll just have to see," he said. "We have to test it out. You see, we don't really *know* what it was, do we? It may have been *just* the elixir. . . ."

Lawrence was aghast, then defensive. "*Or* it may have been *just* my fake false fox scent!"

"Well, that's what we have to see," said Anthony W-B, keeping very calm and scientific. "And there

The Escape of the Giant Hogstalk

are a few other things we will have to check out, too."

"Like what?" asked Lawrence, still a bit impatient to get on with it.

"Like if it kills the Giant Hogstalk," Anthony W-B began slowly, *"what else might it kill?"*

Lawrence opened wide eyes in horror. "Oh no!" he cried. "Not . . . like foxes."

"Yes, or like people," said Anthony W-B matter-of-factly, as he finished labeling Lawrence's beakers, "#2" and "#2A." "So first we must take one beaker of the elixir and find another Hogstalk, and pour it over it."

So Lawrence and Anthony W-B started westward over the high field toward the low field that led to the brook. It was a good place to hunt for Hogstalks and they were not disappointed. A smallish Hogstalk —not over five feet high—was growing close to the edge of the brook.

"And there's another!" cried Lawrence, sighting an even larger Hogstalk down the bank a bit.

The Escape of the Giant Hogstalk

"Very well," said Anthony W-B. "We're in luck. This is a very nearly perfect setup. An outdoor laboratory, so to speak." Then, being very careful not to touch the plant, he poured the contents of beaker #1 around the roots of the smaller Hogstalk and sprinkled some on the leaves. The thirsty plant drank it up.

Anthony W-B and Lawrence just stood by and watched, waiting for the Hogstalk to fold up as the other had done. They waited ten minutes. Nothing. If anything, the plant looked better. "This may have something in it that I'll need for my final Elixir of Life," muttered Anthony W-B. "I think that plant grew a bit while we were here."

"I'm sure it did," said Lawrence. "Okay, it didn't work. So it's probably the fake false fox scent that did it. Right?"

"Maybe," said Anthony W-B as they made their way back to the laboratory, "and maybe not. That's science, old boy. Can't be sure until it's demonstrated."

The Escape of the Giant Hogstalk

Back at the laboratory they picked up beaker #2, which was the fake false fox scent, and carried it carefully up over the high meadow, down through the low field to the brook. They located the second Giant Hogstalk, just downstream from the one that had drunk the elixir. That one was really thriving. But now they turned their attention to applying the contents of beaker #2 to the second Hogstalk.

"Say, Tony, let me do it, please. It's my formula, you know," Lawrence begged.

"Right," said Anthony W-B, "but be careful not to touch the plant."

Lawrence very carefully sprinkled some fox scent over the leaves of the Hogstalk, and the rest over the roots. And then they waited. And they waited. And they waited.

"I'll tell you something, Lawrence," said Anthony W-B, "I think you're getting pretty close to that fake false fox scent. That almost has a real foxy-type smell. It might fool some *people*, but I'm not so sure it would fool a dog."

The Escape of the Giant Hogstalk

Lawrence was pleased. He had nearly forgotten about the original purpose of the scent in all the excitement. "What do you think it needs, Tony?"

"Can't be sure. Maybe more turp . Have to try it on some dogs."

"Or maybe just some more *Luxurie #10*," said Lawrence, who rather liked the smell.

"Well, let's hope not," said Anthony W-B. "That stuff costs about five pounds the half-ounce! Anyhow, all you need to do is keep trying. And so do I," he added sadly. Then he brightened. "Still, I haven't really given that last elixir, with the calcium propionate, a chance. I just have a feeling I'm on the right track there. Well," he looked at his watch, "that's fifteen minutes and that Hogstalk looks just fine. Back to the lab!"

They took the shortcut through the woods, though the walking was harder, and it brought them right to the back of the laboratory where the collapsed Hogstalk lay. And Lawrence noticed something interesting.

The Escape of the Giant Hogstalk

"Tony," he said. "You were saying that the stuff we mixed up might kill foxes and like that. Right?"

"Right," said Anthony W-B. "That's another part of the experiment, of course."

"Well then," Lawrence was excited. "How come it hasn't killed any of the other *plants*? Look, there are some ferns and there are some bluebells, and all that grass. . . ."

Anthony W-B surveyed the scene. "By George, Lawrence! What a clever lad you are! You may make a better scientist than I. You're right, of course. I hadn't even noticed it. Lawrence, it is just barely possible that we may have discovered not only the way to rid the country of the Giant Hogstalk: we may have discovered an entirely selective weed killer! That is, if it kills only the Hogstalk and nothing else . . . not a blade of grass . . . wow!" And that was a lot of enthusiasm for Anthony W-B.

They both turned and rushed into the cottage, squeezing through the door together in their hurry, knocking over a few jars and bottles as they made

The Escape of the Giant Hogstalk

their way to the laboratory table. Anthony W-B picked up beaker #1A and Lawrence picked up beaker #2A and together they poured them into one large beaker. Anthony W-B divided that into two beakers. Then, carrying one of the beakers, they hurried as fast as they dared, over the high field, down through the low field, and to the brook where both Hogstalks were standing.

"I'd swear, Tony, this thing is even bigger now. Look, it's nearly as tall as you are."

"I think they spring up while you're not looking," said Anthony W-B. "Isn't that another one over there?" And there was, indeed, a third Hogstalk in sight. But now the real moment of truth was upon them. They both held their breath while Anthony W-B sprinkled and poured the contents of beaker #1A plus #2A over the Hogstalk.

"And they flop down while you look at them!" cried Lawrence, hopping around on one foot. Because, actually, as the Hogstalk greedily drank the elixir and fake false fox scent, it started to change.

The Escape of the Giant Hogstalk

First its head bent, then it leaned a little, then it folded over once, twice, three times, and sank to the ground.

"Merciful heavens!" said Anthony W-B, back to his old self. "Lawrence, we have just conducted a controlled experiment which proves that it is the combination of our two formulas that has produced this unusual product which could rid the country of the Giant Hogstalk. Only one thing remains to be done, and we must do it immediately."

"What's that?" asked Lawrence.

"We must try it on a living creature—a mouse."

"Oh no, Tony! You can't do that. You might kill it."

"That's the point, old boy."

"But you can't *try* and kill something."

"I'm not going to try and *kill* it. I'm going to use one of my mice to *experiment* on. That's the way it has to be done. It's a chance we have to take. We don't want to have something that might hurt the people who use this, do we?"

"No," said Lawrence reluctantly. They were on

their way back to the laboratory now. "But does the mouse have to drink it?"

Anthony W-B thought that over. "No," he said, finally. "Now that you mention it, we use all sorts of things every day that would certainly hurt us if we drank them or ate them, but are harmless to touch or breathe. No. The mouse won't have to drink the potion." Lawrence was relieved.

They entered the laboratory, but this time Lawrence was in no hurry and let Anthony W-B go in first. Lawrence stared out the window while Anthony W-B sprinkled one of the mice with Potion #1A Plus #2A (which they felt was a good name for the stuff). Then Anthony W-B put the mouse in a separate little wooden cage. Then, as an extra test, he took another mouse and put him in a glass cage. Then he put some of the potion into a spray can and sprayed it all around in the glass cage. While he was at it, he caught a few flies and put them in the glass cage, too.

"This is certainly the most efficiently run and the

quickest experiment that I have ever conducted," said Anthony W-B with a sort of confidence that he had not really felt before. "Come on, Lawrence, we'll go up to the house for a bit of tea and then come back and see what's what."

After tea Lawrence pushed Anthony ahead of him. "You look," he said. "I'll wait out here."

"What kind of scientist are you going to make if you can't face up to the necessary tasks? Come on."

So Lawrence forced himself to follow Anthony W-B into the laboratory, and he squinted his eyes half shut so he could see just a little.

The first mouse in the wooden cage was busy trying to find his way out of it and back to the big one he had come from where all his friends were. "He's fine," Anthony W-B said. The second mouse in the glass cage was a worry at first, but then it turned out he was just having a nap. In pure gratitude Lawrence gave him the biscuit he had saved from tea. As for the flies, they were zipping around without a hint of any disability.

The Escape of the Giant Hogstalk

Anthony W-B seemed to grow a few inches taller himself . . . not unlike the Giant Hogstalk. "Lawrence," he said, "this potion can be manufactured in large quantities from these same simple ingredients and sprayed on the fields and marshes from all kinds of sprayers. That should get at the Hogstalks this year. Next year any young seedlings can be treated the same way. Within no time we shall have beaten the problem." Then Anthony W-B sat down and picked up his formula and Lawrence's formula. Then he picked up the telephone. "Kindly connect me with the Society of Royal Biologists," he said to the operator. "And hurry!"

"Anthony Wilson-Brown, in the name of the Queen, I declare you a member of the Society of Royal Biologists . . ." the Chief Biologist was saying.

Anthony W-B half rose from his red velvet chair. "But I *am* a member," he protested.

" . . . Eradication Division," continued the Chief Biologist, looking at his notes. Then he pinned a shin-

ing new gold medal on Anthony W-B. "Wait till I get my Elixir of Life," Anthony W-B thought to himself.

"Lawrence Rockford, in the name of the Queen, I declare you the youngest provisional member of the Society of Royal Biologists," droned the Chief Biologist, and he pinned a similar gold medal on Lawrence.

"Wait till I really get my fake false fox scent," Lawrence said to himself.

The Chief Biologist—who seemed to have gotten a medal himself, somehow, in the proceedings—addressed all the newspapermen and television people. "We now have the problem of the Giant Hogstalk entirely under control," he said, smiling at all angles for each camera.

"Will you be getting rid of the original plant at the Royal Botanic Gardens, then?" asked one of the reporters.

"Certainly not!" said the Chief Biologist. "We

The Escape of the Giant Hogstalk

keep specimens of all kinds of plants—dangerous or not. It's just that this plant was a bit unusual in its . . . er . . . manageability. But, bless my soul, we have it in hand, now."

The Giant Hogstalk now seemed to grow a darker green and it began to hunch again. Some of the old sparring between the keeper and the Hogstalk was revived. "It's plotting," Oliver Buskin had the bad sense to say to the Orchid Keeper, who answered by tapping his head lightly. "Potty!" he muttered. "Plotting," said Buskin, who was getting a bit hard of hearing. And he would not and did not change his mind. Anyone with an eye could see that the Giant Hogstalk was biding its time.